Tales from the West of Ireland

Published in 1999 by
Mercier Press
5 French Church Street Cork
Tel: (021) 275040; Fax (021) 274969
E-mail: books@mercier.ie
16 Hume Street Dublin 2
Tel: (01) 661 5299; Fax: (01) 661 8583
E-mail: books@marino.ie

Trade enquiries to CMD Distribution
55A Spruce Avenue
Stillorgan Industrial Park
Blackrock County Dublin
Tel: (01) 294 2556; Fax: (01) 294 2564

ISBN 1 85635 268 4

10 9 8 7 6 5 4 3 2 1

A CIP record for this title is available
from the British Library

Cover design by Liam Furlong
Printed in Ireland by ColourBooks,
Baldoyle Industrial Estate, Dublin 13

Tales from the West of Ireland

Sean Henry

CONTENTS

FOREWORD

I have made no attempt to classify the ensuing tales. I can vouch for the truth of some tales myself, while most of the remainder were related to me by people who genuinely believed in their authenticity.

Sean Henry

BLIAIN NA bhFRANNCACH

When the little French expeditionary force under General Humbert landed at Kilcummin, near Killala, north Mayo on 22 August 1798, they were received with open arms by the local people who looked on their coming as a whole-hearted attempt by Napoleon to free Ireland from English domination. They would not have dreamed of regarding it as an operation to divert a sizeable amount of England's land and sea forces from theatres of war on the Continent.

The ensuing campaign, resulting in the capture of Ballina and then Castlebar and the clearing of County Mayo of all enemy forces by the Franco-Irish force, was a brilliant opening to the short-lived insurrection in the west. The fatal delay of almost two weeks in Castlebar unfortunately gave the enemy time to regroup and plan counter attacks and encircling movements unhindered.

During the French stay in Castlebar, they were wined and dined on a most lavish scale by the people of the town and the surrounding country-side. The victory of the Franco-Irish forces at Castlebar and the proclamation of the Republic of Connacht under President John Moore now infused new spirit into the people of Castlebar and in the whole country as well. Those who did not come to join for active service came loaded with gifts of meat, butter, poultry, eggs, fish, etc., for the troops. One party came with a steer that had been cooked in a quarry near the town on heated slabs of limestone, a custom dating back to Hannibal's time. Gifts of clothing and footwear donated by merchants from Castlebar and the nearby towns also arrived.

Drilling the raw recruits and getting them accustomed to the French muskets, swords and small arms took up some valuable time. Despite all this, it has been stated that the Irish recruits who stuck to or reverted to their traditional weapon the pike gave a better account of themselves and inspired more fear among the Redcoats at Carricknagat and Ballinamuck, as well as in the capture of Castlebar. As the news of the 'Races of Castlebar' spread like wildfire through the county, batches of raw recruits under their local leaders poured in to the town daily. A large contingent came from the Newport-Ballycroy area. A company from Ballycroy and Erris had previously marched to Ballina to join. A body of insurgents from Westport and Louisburgh included two Augustinian Friars, Fr Myles Prendergast and Fr Michael Gannon. This force was led by Johnny Gibbons, locally nicknamed Johnny the Outlaw.

From the Knock-Aughamore district came two strong companies under Captain Seamas O'Malley and Richard Jordan. A company of recruits came from Killedan and Bohola parishes under Henry Valentine Jordan of Rosslevin. A large company from the glens around Nephin Mountain who joined on the route from Ballina to Castlebar were led by Captain Peadar Jordan of Coolnabinna. Peadar Jordan escaped to Achill Island after the collapse of the rising and died suddenly while on the run there. He composed the poem *Cúl na Binn*, one of the finest poems of the '98 period. It may be mentioned that one of the martyred priests of the Penal Days in east Mayo was Fr Fulgentius Jordan, so the Jordans should hold an honoured place in the turbulent history of Mayo.

Another local leader who joined the Franco-Irish force (just before the fight for Castlebar) with a strong body of pikemen was Captain Willie Mangan of Sion Hill. The first rout of any of the Redcoat regiments guarding the approaches to Castlebar took place at Sion Hill, according to local tradition. This, coupled with a flanking attack from the west side of the town by about three hundred pikemen, is believed to be the main factor in the complete rout of England's regular soldiers and the hated Irish militia.

Four years previously, the people of Castlebar and the neighbourhood had flocked into Main Street to watch two wine-soaked rackrenting landlords fight or attempt to fight a sword duel. Caesar French of Oughterard and the local bully boy George Robert (or as he was nicknamed Fighting) Fitzgerald of Turlough House were the contestants. During the scuffle, Fitzgerald's spurs got entangled in his great coat and he fell to the ground. Immediately Frencn placed his foot on Fitzgerald's chest and pointed his sword at his throat with the familiar duellist's demand to surrender or die. Then the crowd surged forward to save their local oppressor with the result that French had to flee for his life. He wisely had his attendant waiting with two saddled horses at the top of the town and lost no time in fleeing for his life towards Oughterard.

One of the few landlords who led a company of 'United' recruits to Castlebar was John Moore of Ballintaffy (midway between Claremorris and Kiltimagh). Four years previously, John Moore with his landlord neighbours, John Joyce of Oxford House and Thomas Ormsby of Ballinamore, sat on the jury that found Fighting Fitzgerald guilty of the murder of another landiord, Randal McDonnell of Windsor House, Castlebar. The jury were handpicked favourites of Denis Browne, the County Sheriff, later to be known as *Donncha an Rópa*. Browne saw in Fitzgerald (an influential landlord and nephew of the Earl of Bristol and Bishop of Derry) an enemy to be elminated at all costs, and he did not hide his happiness when Fitzgerald was executed. Seeing one of his hand-picked jurors side with the rebels caused him to have a secret tunnel constructed from his house (now the Convent of Mercy, Claremorris) to a grove of trees some distance away as an escape hatch in case of a rebel victory.

On their march from Castlebar to Ballinamuck, the French and Irish force marched through Bohola direct to Swinford. The Castlebar-Swinford main road at that time joined the Swinford-Kiltimagh main road at Carrabawn, a mile from Swinford and it was over this road that Humbert entered Swinford. When a historian Dr Hayes travelled to Castlebar, Swinford, and over Humbert's march to

Longford in general nearly fifty years ago he was wrongly informed on this point. He was told in Swinford that Humbert marched to Foxford and then to Swinford. Such a route would involve a detour of fifteen or sixteen miles, two unnecessary crossings of the River Moy and a march through mountainy foothills which would be ideal ambush terrain for enemy units. This to seasoned campaigners like Humbert or Blake the Irish commander would have been unthinkable. General Humbert and his aides Sarrazin and Charcot dined in Anthony Corley's Hotel, now O'Hagan's, on the square in Swinford. The French leader first called a halt and, after sentries were posted and scouting parties sent out, ordered the troops into a large field, part of which is now the vocational school grounds. Two steers donated by Brabazon the local landlord and two more donated or taken from the Bohola landlord McManus were hastily prepared and roasted. Four large iron gates belonging to Brabazon were used for roasting grids over large turf fires. Having eaten, the troops marched on to Bellaghy. There one of their flanking parties, sent out the day before leaving Castlebar, rode up with the news that large enemy forces lay directly between them and the River Shannon. This decided Humbert to change course in the hope of outflanking his enemies and getting into the central plain and hopefully on to Dublin via the upper reaches of the Shannon. The troops halted and camped for the night in a field on the Sligo side of Bellaghy earlier than intended in order to be on the march to Tubbercurry and Collooney in good time the following morning. At Carricknagat, near Collooney, a small enemy force under Colonel Vereker (ancestor of Lord Gort, British Army Commander-in-Chief, forty years ago) mounted an attack on the Franco-Irish force from a strategic position. Their lone cannon was wreaking havoc, especially on the Irish section of the force until a lone horseman rode out from the Irish ranks and by steering a zig-zag course rode to within a few paces of the English gunner and shot him dead. Vereker then sounded the retreat and fell back on Sligo.

The lone horseman, Teeling, executed by the enemy after the final collapse of the rising, has streets named in his honour in different western towns. Just before the action at Carricknagat, the French and Irish force were augmented by a contingent of pikemen from Coolcarney (Attymass) and Bonniconlon under Colonel O'Dowd, a retired veteran of the wars on the Continent. This force, which had marched through the Windy Gap and the foothills of the Ox Mountains, gave a good account of themselves at Carricknagat and three days later at Ballinamuck. An old song of the period contains the lines –

Chuaigh sinn go Cúl Chearnaí 'gus ar aghaidh 'mach an Bearna
A's an Dúbhdach Mór mar Fhronntach sinn d'ár dtreorígh.

An Dúbhdach Mór was Colonel O'Dowd and the *Bearna* was the Windy Gap west of Lough Talt.

Having crossed the Shannon at Ballintra, it

became apparent to Humbert that he was left with no choice but to give battle with enemy forces closing in and harrassing his men with increasing intensity. Ballinamuck and the ridge of Shanmullagh was far from being the ideal place to make a stand, but surrounded on all sides by forces estimated to number 25,000 seasoned troops, he had little choice. The pikemen retreating broke repeated charges of crack cavalrymen by sticking the heels of their pikes into the ground at the last moment and impaling the horses and sometimes the riders. Humbert's hasty surrender after a short exchange of fire and the 'chivalrous' treatment of himself and his staff by the English commanders was in sharp contrast to the fate of his Irish allies. Left to fight on their own, their stubborn fight earned tributes from some of their enemies. The French force at Ballinamuck has been estimated at about nine hundred men. There are no definite figures of the Irish casualities at Ballinamuck. It is believed that three hundred dead, four hundred taken prisoner and another four hundred escaped would be a reasonable figure. The numbers taken prisoner were considerably reduced by the mass executions of prisoners, not alone at Ballinamuck, but in every town and village along the route of Humbert's march from Killala to Longford. It is generally believed, but this is not confirmed officially, that General George Blake of Garracloon (Ballinrobe), the Irish commander at Ballinamuck, was hanged immediately after the fighting ceased. With martial law and unauthorised killings by the victors being a regular pattern of life in Ireland for three years or more after the rising, it is of course impossible to place a figure on the casualities connected with that Continental invasion of Ireland. It must also be remembered that records were scanty and unreliable, especially in relation to Tone's 'men of no property' who were not fully regarded as human beings by the victorious army of occupation.

THE AFTERMATH

Writers have often commented on the difficulty of obtaining reliable information in the west of Ireland on events connected with the '98 rising, in comparison to County Wexford and other Leinster counties. Unfortunately the big answer to this question is the famine. In Mayo and in the west in general, not alone whole families, but whole villages with all their history, folklore and customs were wiped out. The famine did not make such an impact on more prosperous thinly populated counties like Wexford, Wicklow, Carlow and Kildare. Many farms in those counties remain in the possession of direct descendants of people who took part in or witnessed events connected with 1798. Many of the Mayo men who escaped from the massacre of Ballinamuck were Gaelic speakers and were between one hundred and fifty and two hundred miles from their native heath. To add to their woes, the River Shannon lay between them and home and it was well watched and guarded to prevent their return. Ill clad and ill shod with winter around the corner, their lot was not a happy one. There is a tale of a Shannon boatman who rowed two loads of Mayo men across the river one night shortly after the fight of Ballinamuck. Only on his deathbed a few years later could he dare mention the matter, as blood money and spies were plentiful for years after '98. There was another story of the Roscommon woman living near the Shannon in 1798 who on a few occasions found her cows milked dry when she collected them for the morning milking. She was afraid to mention the matter to anyone as she guessed that it meant that some Mayo rebels had passed during the night or early morning. In 1798 the summer and autumn were finer than average and all the hay and grain crops were collected early. However, the potato stalks remained green until mid-October; this was the favourite hiding ground for the hunted rebels during the day, and they travelled all night.

To make matters worse, most of them had to discard their pikes as being too noticeable and unwieldy. It is no wonder that a high proportion of the Mayo insurgents are just listed as 'never returned'. A few of the insurgents were men who deserted from the Redcoats or militia regiments and when caught, whether armed or not, their fate was sealed. Leaders like General Blake of Garracloon and Colonel O'Dowd of Bonniconlon and Colonel Bellew of Killala, trained veteran soldiers, were executed without semblance of a trial. Colonel McDonnell of Carracon, who was wounded at the capture of Castlebar, escaped to France, refused promotion by Napoleon and went to America where he died. One of the Murrisk Abbey Friars who joined the United men (insurgents), Fr Michael Gannon, escaped to France in a French officer's uniform and rose to high rank in the French army. The other Friar, Myles Prendergast, escaped to Connemara along with Johnny Gibbons and a few more United men. A verse of a song attributed to the poet Raftery runs –

Tá Johnny Gibbons 'gus ár n-athair Maolmhuire
'Gus a chomplacht fiór amach san mhóin
Faoi thárt, faoi easanair, a's fuacht na hoíche
Agus deamhan braon di acu ná dram le n-ól.

Ar n-athair Maolmhuire was of course Fr Myles Prendergast. He never returned from Connemara, where he died fifty years after the rebellion. Johnny Gibbons was captured by the Redcoats with the aid of a spy who had damped the powder in Johnny's pistols to complete his downfall. When Johnny saw his pistols useless and the house encircled by his enemies, he exclaimed: *'Tá Johnny i nead lachan 'gus a mhéar i bpoll tráthair'*. (Johnny is in a duck's nest and his finger in an augerhole.) This saying lived on to describe anybody in a tight corner. Packing victims' fingers into grooved augerholes was a form of punishment in those days and ducks' nests were so constructed that the ducks could not leave until released. Duck eggs were too valuable as a food in those days of continuous privation to allow the ducks to lay out in ponds or rivers.

When Johnny Gibbons was executed in Castlebar, his godfather Denis Browne, *Donncha an Rópa*, took pleasure in being present as he had previously been when his sworn enemy Fighting Fitzgerald had been executed some years earlier.

Captain Mangan of Sion Hill was killed a few years after the rising just when a free pardon was being prepared for a number of insurgents. Local tradition says that his fate was encompassed by a spy who felled him with a stone after he had got through a ring of soliders at Letter, near Nephin. Among those who are listed as 'never returned' are John Moore of Ballintaffy, Henry Jordan of Rosslevin and Seamus Dubh Horkan of Rathscanlon, Swinford. (Henry Jordan is believed to have died in Connemara.) Among those who went from Swinford with Seamus Dubh Horkan to join up in Castlebar were Paddy Brennan, a blacksmith who forged the pikes for the local United Irishmen, and Seamas Durkin, a tailor. Durkin had his workshop in what is now the local Garda Station. Durkin's grandfather was a landlord locally known as *Muiris na Muaidh* (Maurice of the Moy). Muiris lived a half mile south of Cloonacanana ford on the River Moy. The walls of his dwelling still stand close to the main Swinford-Aclare Road.

Muiris na Muaidh was the landlord of the nine townlands nearest to Cloonacanana ford. He fought as a young officer in the Irish Army at Aughrim, one of the bloodiest battles in Irish history. After Aughrim he lost most of his lands in the Williamite confiscations. Admittedly he was not fighting for Ireland's freedom. He was fighting, like his commander Patrick Sarsfield, Earl of Lucan, for the right of the poltroon English King James II to rule Ireland in preference to William of Orange. Incidentally he was, of course, fighting for his landed estates. Ironically the Vatican supported William of Orange.

Seamas Durkin escaped from the massacre of Ballinamuck and found refuge in a disused sandpit in a large field, from which he saw the Redcoats searching along the hedgerows around the field. After nightfall he headed in an easterly direction, luckily for himself, as all routes to the west were well watched. After some days, he found shelter and employment with a farmer in a quiet spot thirty miles from Ballinamuck. Some time afterwards, he went back to his old trade and worked from place to place as a journeyman tailor. It was almost three years after '98 before he returned home. He built a small house in the townland of Cloonacanana beside the old fort of Lisconnell. He married a few years later, and I can remember his two daughters Nellie and Winnie. Winnie married a local man, Tom Salmon, and Nellie married Martin Henry of Ballydrum, my paternal grandfather. Grandmother Nellie never fully mastered the English language but for a torrent of invective in Gaelic she was hard to beat. When she died in 1912 she was nearly one hundred years old.

The Mayo priests were executed for complicity or aiding and abetting the insurgents. Fr Manus Sweeney of Achill was executed on the market crane in Newport and Fr Conroy of Addergoole in Castlebar. Another priest Fr Owen Cowley died from ill-health and hardship while on the run. The tree in the Mall on which Fr Conroy was executed was blown down by a storm in 1918. At a huge county anti-conscription meeting in the Mall a few days later De Valera referred to the tree and its history, having been briefed on the matter by local republicans. The priests who sided with the rebels in 1798 were excommunicated. To this day it is believed the fiat or excommunication edict has not been revoked.

It is interesting to note that among the claims lodged for goods etc., seized by the French in and around Swinford was a claim for cattle, wine and spirits by Sir Anthony Brabazon and a claim by Ormsby of Ballinamore for cattle, grass, spirits and a saddle. Brabazon was allowed £146.13.5 and Ormsby £53 (10s.3½d less than he had claimed). A score or more of genuine claims by people who were not dyed-in-the-wool loyalists were either deferred or disallowed by the Commissioners sent to examine the claims. McManus of Bohola, a Catholic landlord was allowed £1,733.18.1d, so it seems that even though a Catholic, his loyalty was not doubted.

GREAT GRANDMOTHER'S TALES

My maternal great grandmother, who died in 1911 and to the best of her reckoning, one hundred and two years old, was a mine of information on events connected with the famine. Unfortunately nobody thought of recording her tales of her early days. Her husband Thomas McDonnell of Ballintaffy,

Claremorris, died a young man in 1847, leaving her with a very young family. In keeping with local custom, the Widow McDonnell was known all her life by her maiden name, Mary McHugh. Her holding of land, being a middleman's holding, was larger than the average and this she regarded as being more of a liability than an asset as the annual rent to her landlord, Ormsby of Ballinamore, was correspondingly high.

At the time of her husband's death, she had four cottiers as small subletters on her holding. Each cottier rented one field with his cottage and tilled it to the utmost. The size of the field varied from one to two acres. Milk was usually supplied by the landowner who let the cottage and field, in return for seasonal assistance with spring and harvesting work. Her landlord allowed her to increase the number of subletters to eight. This, she maintained, meant the difference between security and eviction for her. Their small rents, plus their assistance with her farm work as required, almost paid her rent to the landlord.

She had a rather amusing tale involving her husband. Some time after their marriage, he went to Dublin to lodge some money in a bank, there being no provincial banks at the time. One of his horses was lame and the other one a mare was rearing a foal, so he set off walking at daybreak on a fine summer morning. Some time on the second day, having crossed the Shannon, he got a lift from two men on a horse-drawn miller's dray or low slung cart. He found that his companions could not speak Irish. Luckily for himself he could understand English much better than he could speak it. Between their hints and whispers, he patched up enough of their conversation to realise that they meant to rob and kill him, if necessary, when they came to the wood beyond the next little town. He had donned a new suit and shoes leaving home and this led his companions to believe that he was worth robbing. He planned to jump off the dray when they got to the town.

Hearing an unusual animal-like roar, he looked ahead and saw a donkey drover and a bunch of donkeys approaching along the road. On spotting the horse, one donkey ran forward braying loudly. The horse wheeled around on the road and bolted in the opposite direction at top speed. My great grandfather leaped off the dray and over the fence into a nearby field. He had never seen a donkey before, and judging by their blood-curdling braying, he felt it better to get out of their reach as fast as possible. The drover however hailed him and assured him that his animals were harmless. Seeing a donkey was an experience for him as donkeys were almost unknown in Mayo at the time. When the Napoleonic wars left Ireland almost denuded of horses, they having been snapped up for the Imperial cavalry regiments, English and Scottish donkey dealers saw a ready market in Ireland. They shipped the donkeys in thousands over the short Larne-Stranraer route in flat-bottom boats. He called to a farmhouse shortly afterwards and stayed there overnight. He continued his journey at daybreak the next morning and took care not to fall in with his carter companions again.

The McDonnells kept a bull. In Irish farming circles, a bull rated nearly as high as a hunter or a racehorse as a status symbol. One of the most sustaining foods in those famine days, a mixture of oatmeal and blood known as *Prásán fola*, was expected to sustain a hard-working man for a full day. (A mixture of oatmeal and milk was known as *prásán* and a mixture of oatmeal and butter, which could be moulded into cakes or rolls, was known as *bustán*.) In the McDonnell household, the bull bore the brunt of the bleeding rituals. For some reason, the bleeding operation was always carried out on Sunday afternoons. The widow said that her bull became so accustomed or resigned to the ritual that he uttered the most mournful bellows when he saw his tormentors approaching.

Bleeding was effected by puncturing a vein in the animal's left shoulder. On the final occasion (for the bull), the operation was carried out by a son of the regular 'vet' who was ill. Through some miscalculation, the bleeding could not be stopped and in the excitement the bull broke loose and quickly bled to death from over exertion.

The widow decided to make the best of a bad job. She sent for a regular butcher to Claremorris and got the bull prepared and salted. She found that she had to send a man on horseback to Kilsallagh, Westport, for a bag of salt as she said she could only get pinches of salt locally. The man who sold the salt was known as a panner. He got his salt from trapped sea water by what was known as the shallow pan method. Having salted most of the animal, she found she had enough left to make a feast for her cottiers, relatives and neighbours. and she said that feast, and what they took home, put them over the hungriest spring she ever remembered – 1848.

Watercress was a highly prized piece of food in the famine years. A broad sluggish drain where watercress abounded, midway along the Claremorris-Kiltimagh road, was mentioned by the Widow McDonnell as being black with people eating watercress in the famine years. The edible root of a herb known as the *blioscán* was dug up and eaten raw, as was another herb root known as the *cutharlán* which had a marble sized bulb on the root.

My great-grandmother had vivid memories of turbulent elections and bye-elections around the famine years and later. The candidates, all landlords, were adept at rousing the starving peasantry. In the words of James Connolly, they 'engendered as much heat as was possible into the part of the body politic furthest removed from the idea of social justice'. In one election, Lord Oranmore and Browne, the Tory candidate, was opposed by Kirwan, a Catholic landlord with Repeal sympathies. After 1848, the year of revolutions around the world and the first incipient attempts at democratic upsurge, the English government passed a law that made a defeated election candidate accountable for the victorious candidate's election expenses. This in itself was a blow against democracy as it ensured that only men of substance could seek election. When Lord Oranmore opened his election campaign in Claremorris, he had a kinsman, a son of Donncha an Rópa, on his platform. A local clergyman, Fr Gibbons, led a group who broke up the meeting shouting 'soap the rope' at young Browne. This was one of his father's nicknames.

Lady Oranmore, seeing the election tide flowing against her husband, went to Archbishop McHale and begged him on her knees to turn the tide in favour of her husband. Her husband went around swaggering that the branches of his trees would pay for the election if he lost. Kirwan replied by saying that the hooves and horns of all his cattle would more than pay for the election. Lady Oranmore however realised that her husband was an encumbered landlord. Archbishop McHale acceded to her request and threw his weight behind Oranmore, who won the election. Dr McHale lived to regret his action, as Oranmore proved a strong opponent of any scheme designed to benefit the plain hard-working masses.

OLD ANIMAL CHARMS AND CURES

Two miles west of Bohola along the main road to Castlebar lies the townland of Loughkeeraun. The tiny bogland loch or lake from which the townland got its name has completely disappeared over the past half century owing to local drainage operations. There was an old tradition that St Kieran cured a valuable cow that was dying with water taken from the loch and because of this the loch was a popular place of pilgrimage for centuries. Pilgrims came to Loch Kieran mainly to pray for luck and prosperity with their livestock in the forthcoming year. Not to be outdone in religious fervour, or whatever, some pilgrims took rolls of butter to throw into the lake as an offering to the saint. More practical local people came later and salvaged the rolls of butter. Having recycled the butter, it was packed into their butter firkins and sold in the Swinford butter market. I can remember pilgrims going to Loch Kieran on 15 August, which seemed to be the most popular date of all for local pilgrimages in this country.

For a kicking cow, a popular cure was to get two people to pass a buring sod of turf under and over the standing cow in the names of Saints Patrick, Bridget and Colmcille.

For a newly calved heifer cow to give butter-rich milk, a similar ritual was performed. In this case, the lighted turf sod was passed around the cow's back legs in the names of the Blessed Trinity. I can remember on one occasion, while assisting an aunt in this operation, the cow showed her disapproval by kicking the burning sod into a bundle of straw, almost setting fire to the byre. Having been rebuked for laughing, I was told that the fire was blessed. However, I felt that the ritual was more of pagan than Christian origin.

In some districts down to the present day, giving away milk on May Day was forbidden as it was regarded as giving away one's luck for the rest of the year. Giving away fire on that day was also taboo. I recall a story by an old neighbouring woman who absent-mindedly went to borrow a coal on May morning when she found her fire had gone out. Her return trip was done in record time without the coal of fire.

Some years ago, I called to a well-known County Mayo chemist for a remedy for calf scour. I mentioned to him that in my neighbourhood people of old had great faith in the soup of boiled briar roots for this ailment. The chemist said that tannin was a popular agent for contracting the lower bowel to arrest scour. Briar root, he said, contained a high percentage of tannin.

In bygone times, beef and butter were the most important items in rural economy – as they are at the present time. Anybody found trespassing on a neighbour's land on May Day might be suspected of gathering certain lucky herbs in order to take the neighbour's luck. If the trespasser could be heard saying the words *'im agus bainne 'gâm'* when plucking herbs on another man's land, he was in real danger.

The use of the dead hand to bring luck in butter gathering is happily a thing of the past. The last known instance of anything in that line being practised in Mayo was over a hundred years ago at a point where the three parishes of Killedàn, Knock and Kilcolman join, almost midway between Claremorris, Kiltimagh and Knock. An old woman who lived alone was being waked in the year 1850. A frightening thunderstorm sprang up during the night which so frightened all at the wake that they all rushed out and away home. When some of them returned the following morning, they found that the old woman's right hand had been severed and taken away. I heard this tale being told by an old man, John Hynes, over fifty years ago. His father was one of those who attended the old woman's wake.

In some cases, animal help was invoked to cure human ailments. Donkey's milk and ferret's (food) leavings, together with the fasting spit and boiled primroses, were time-honoured cures for jaundice and other mystery complaints. Some of those confirm the saying of the cure being worse than the ailment.

MATCHMAKING AND ELOPEMENTS

The arranging of marriages and all the mediation and diplomacy involved was known in Ireland as matchmaking. It was regarded by many as an old Gaelic custom. It was in reality a product of hard economic realities begotten by alien repression, the landlord system, the famine and the repeal of the of the corn laws, which some economists regarded as a greater economic blow to the country than the famine. This law gave first claim to the estate, farm or property involved to the oldest son of the family. In return he was expected to provide dowries, or fortunes, to use a more common term, for sisters and sometimes brothers as required. Sometimes when the oldest son was in line to get married, he was approaching the 'sere and yellow leaf' stage. To make matters more complicated, he often had a sister still on hand, waiting for his intended wife's fortune to take to her future husband. This future husband often had a sister waiting for this fortune to take away with her and so *ad infinitum*. I heard in my young days of a fortune of forty pounds in a nearby parish that was in this manner instrumental in concluding six marriages before finally coming to anchor.

During the famine years, when money all but disappeared, runaway marriages or elopements gained momentum as an alternative to the match-making system. These marriages, while generally frowned on by parents and relatives of the bride and groom, were often secretly welcomed by the oldest son as it helped to let him off the hook from the financial angle. Many of the runaway couples, if they had the few pounds required, headed for England or America and were married by a priest they found agreeable enough to waive minor regulations in their favour. In many other cases, the runaway couple found a willing relative to hide away the prospective bride until, as often happened, the outraged parents of the bride or groom relented to save the family honour and in a good many cases, to save the fortune that would otherwise be expected. I can faintly recall an old shanachie, Seán Mór, in my young days telling of elopements or runaway marriages as he called them.

'I can remember,' he said, 'of my father telling me all about the time around the year 1850 when Máire Wee (Bhuídhe) and Seán Bán, who lived in that tumble down house below the crossroad, ran away, God rest them both. Máire came from Carrick-na-Gower, over there at the top of the mountain. Her parents had notions and did not think Séán or his holding here in Shraigh good enough for them, or may be it was all pretentions.

'After all hopes of getting her parents or even his own to give in failed, Seán and Máire decided to run away. On the night Seán came to take her off with him, there was snow on the ground and he carried her down the mountainside on his back. Her neighbours said afterwards the tracks of her two big toes were visible on the snow the next day, as she was much taller than Seán. To lend more evidence to the tale, she carried her only pair of shoes wrapped up in the pocket of her coat, to save them for her hoped-for marriage. Seán left her with a sympathetic old bachelor uncle of his, hoping that her parents would relent. He felt he would get around his own parents more easily. The two sets of parents foamed and threatened and nearly went back to the flood to find some tale from the past to fling at each other. In spite of all, Máire's parents made no attempt to find her. They could easily track her in the frozen snow if they wanted. After some days of ructions, Máire's parents gave in and allowed the marriage to go ahead. In this way, the family name was saved and the gossips silenced. They managed to save Máire's fortune as well, as I heard they never gave a penny to her and Seán.'

When someone listening to the shanachie in the visiting house asked him did Seán and Máire live happily ever after: 'I am not sure of that,' said the shanachie. 'They were only a short time married when Máire cut her finger. The old cure in those days for a cut, and a good cure it was, was a spider's cobweb. After a search around the house, they could not find a cobweb. "God be with my father's house," said Máire, "you would not be searching all day to find a cobweb." "On the night," said Séan, "that you left the track of your toes on the mountainside, you were glad to get away from your father and his cobwebs."

'On one occasion,' said the shanachie, 'my father was home from the fair with Seán and Máire. He asked Máire if she would rather live in Spraigh than in her native Carrick-na-Gower. "To tell the truth," said Máire, "Good Friday in Carrick-na-Gower was better than Christmas day in Shraigh."'

SCRAWING AND BURNING

In the short spell between the famine years 1845-1848 and the repeal of the corn laws by the British government in 1851, the peasants of Ireland changed over in a big way to the production of grain crops, chiefly oats. They saw the futility of placing too much reliance on the potato as a main tillage crop. Unfortunately they continued and intensified an old custom connected with tillage known as 'Scrawing and Burning'. This involved cutting away or stripping the top grassy or heathery sods of the field intended for cultivation. Those surface sods or scraws were dried and piled into heaps which were set afire and allowed to smoulder to heaps of ashes. The ashes were later spread on the land in the mistaken belief that it was a first class fertiliser. This practice, as time proved, only impoverished the land. Forty years ago, a man named John Drudy, who had been well versed in local history and traditions, showed me fields in his native village of Glann, Charlestown, to prove a point. He said the fields in question, after nearly one hundred years of good care and treatment, were only recovering from the effects of scrawing and burning.

The skimming off of the tough surface scraws with heavy spades or loys was hard laborious work, and it was unfortunate that it was so much labour in vain. I heard a local joke about a father and son in those days who had spent the whole day scrawing and came in to their evening meal around nightfall. This meal and a breakfast of which two boiled duck eggs apiece were the main feature were all that stood for sustenance in those times. There were no tea breaks or other perks of that kind. The father and son's main meal was a large plate of Indian meal porridge laid down between them. This yellow meal was generally known as yellow buck. The son sat down first, and as the stirabout was hot, he began skimming off all the cooler outside part with his spoon. When his father objected, he replied, 'I can be scrawing, Father, and you can be burning.'

At that time, distilleries and malting houses were a feature of the economic life of many provincial towns in Ireland. At the malting houses, the grain was bought from the farmers and prepared for the distilleries. While not absorbing near as much of the grain grown in the country as the mills, they helped to stabilise prices. The repeal of the corn laws in 1851 was a cruel blow just as economic conditions were slowing improving after the disastrous famine. This law allowed the dumping of foreign grain into the country free of tax or any restrictions. This grain, chiefly Indian corn and meal from the United States and wheat from Canada imported at low prices, put many Irish millers out of business and also most of the distilleries and malting houses. Oat production declined and emigration from Ireland which had been slowing down began to escalate again.

One of the last malting houses in Mayo to close was located in Upper Mount Street, Claremorris. Some years before they closed, they advertised in a Dublin newspaper for an experienced maltster. A Dublin man who gave the name of Doyle got the job. He proved to be very talkative and boastful over his drinks. As the first manifestation of famine began to appear, he openly advocated rebellion as the only remedy left to the people. He told them of being out in 1798 and in 1803 with Robert Emmet. He would dramatically exclaim, with a far-away look in his eyes 'Ah! Them were the days.'

The local parson in Claremorris at the time was the Rev. Darcy Sirr. He was a son of the notorious British army town major in Dublin around 1798, Major Sirr who did more than his share in the hounding down of Lord Edward Fitzgerald and the

'98 leaders in Dublin and played a similar role with Robert Emmet and his comrades five years later. Having heard the maltster Doyle blowing his trumpet on one occasion, the Rev. Darcy Sirr felt that he had seen the man and heard the voice before. By degrees it dawned on him that he had seen the man many years ago in his father's house handling some papers with the Major. He also remembered that the man's name was Duggan. He searched among his father's papers, most of which he had taken with him to Mayo. (He later gave those papers over to be filed away or published as the authorities saw fit.) When he found the papers he felt would clear up the identity of Doyle alias Duggan, he sent for the man in question, saying he would be obliged if he called on the following Sunday to his house. When the maltster called, the parson told him to be seated while he went to his study. When he returned, he laid a paper before his visitor on the table. Pointing to a signature at the foot of the document, he said, 'Do you recognise that signature, Duggan?'

Duggan seemed stunned for a few moments. He then stood up and went silently out, returned to town and then turned left on the Ballyhaunis road and probably on to Dublin. He was never seen in Claremorris again. The document the Rev. Sirr laid before Duggan was an acknowledgement of having on a certain date received the sum of fifty guineas from Major Sirr for information which 'helped in the capture of Robert Emmet'. The document carried the signature of James Duggan and was counter-signed by Major Sirr.

Incidentally a few years later another man connected with the 1803 uprising drifted to Mayo. Barney Moran, Robert Emmet's executioner, came to Mayo a penniless mendicant. Despised and disowned by the government he served so slavishly he died in Ballina workhouse fifty years after Emmet's rising.

THE BELLMEN

Up to forty years ago, nearly every town in Ireland could boast of one or more town criers or bellmen, as they were more generally called. Now they are fast becoming only a memory. It seems strange that a segment of the community with so many colourful characters in its ranks down through the years can evoke such little notice of its passing out parade.

Nowadays with more advance notices and ever-increasing advertising in newspapers, television and radio, public address systems, printed handbills, etc., the crier or bellman is no longer required to get the message across, to use a modern slang phrase.

It seems possible that the criers may have been part of the economic life of the country for at least two hundred years in their own way. When the French invasion force landed at Killala, in 1798, the town crier in Ballina, eight miles away, went on the streets of Ballina a few hours later announcing that Napoleon had landed near Killala. A month later, when Lord Roden's Foxhunters and other Redcoat troops returned to retake Ballina and Killala, the Ballina crier was arrested. He would have shared the fate of the United men, Walsh, Barrett and others executed, only that an officer of the notorious north Mayo Militia vouched that he was 'stupid and harmless', and would believe any story he was told.

One of my earliest recollections is listening to a Swinford crier Patsy Cox, locally known as Patcheen, ringing his bell and announcing the coming of a circus to town. Patsy Cox was a child of three years when the famine hit Swinford in 1847. He was taken to Swinford workhouse together with his parents, all stricken down with the dreaded fever that left little hope for famine victims. Two or three days later he was carried out with a dozen more to be buried in a mass grave. After the first showerful of earth was flung in over the victims, the infant Patsy stirred his feeble hand slightly. Luckily one of the grave attendants noticed the movement and took him back to the workhouse again. He recovered and grew up to be a fit able youngster, as he got better inmate treatment by the Workhouse staff who regarded his escape from death and burial as a miracle. Over five hundred famine victims were buried in mass graves in an elevated spot beside the modern Swinford hospital. Those victims came from the Swinford Poor Law Union Area, which embraced all east Mayo and extended to the Lung River in County Roscommon at that time.

In the closing years of the last century and the

opening decades of the present century, a keen rivalry existed in Kiltimagh between two local bellmen: John Forde better known as Jack Straw, and Tom McNicholas, known as Tom Thrasher. He derived the title from his father who was a noted thresher of oats with the old time flail.

The flail, now passing into the limbo of forgotten things, consisted of a five foot by one and a quarter inch stick called the *colpán*, which was loosely attached to a shorter stick called the *buailteán* (or beater). The two sticks were joined by a tie of rope or strip of calico called the *fuang*. Gripping the *colpán* firmly in his hands, the thresher swung the *buailteán* over his head in a circular motion to give more impetus to his blow before bringing it down on the sheaf to be threshed. The most satisfactory timber for the *colpán* was said to be hazel; for the *buailteán* holly. One of the old Celtic legends mentions St Patrick meeting Oisín of the Old Fenian school of warriors. Among other things St Patrick showed Oisín was Oscar, busily employed in the lower regions. He was engaged threshing the devils with an iron flail. (He had been noted thresher in Ireland of old.) Every time he had the devils well cornered for better results, the *fuang* of his flail snapped and he had to start all over again. As Oisín stood watching, St Patrick said he would grant him one wish, expecting he would ask that Oscar be delivered from the lower regions. Oisín immediately replied, 'I wish Oscar had a *fuang* on his flail that would never break.'

Tom Thrasher's father threshed a good sized stack of oats daily with Tom turning the sheaves for him, and their combined pay was four shillings and two meals per day.

Jack Straw was a less aggressive type and had spent a short term in college in his youth. During the Land War days, ballads applauding the fight of the tenants and condemning the landlords and the authorities were classed as seditious. To prevent the circulation of those ballads, the R.I.C. were ordered to prevent the ballad singers and vendors selling those ballads. Bellmen were the chief sellers of ballads, with other sidelines such as peddling matches, shoe laces, pins and needles and other everyday household necessities.

John Forde circumvented the government order by carrying a bunch of oaten straw for which he charged his ballad customers a half penny each, giving them a free ballad and saying at the same time, 'I'll sell my straw and I'll defy the law.' From this incident he got the name Jack Straw. During the Boer War years, Jack was progressive enough to get a peep show lantern which showed pictures of the war and the combatants for which he charged a half-penny a peep.

On one occasion the Claremorris bellman Padneen Kane told Tom Thrasher he had 'a good mind to get married' and asked his advice.

Tom said, 'You have no house or land, not even a garden and I suppose you have no money?'

'No,' replied Padneen.

Having pretended to give the problem serious consideration, Tom said, 'Go ahead and get married; you can't be much worse off than you are.'

ACHILL BREEZES

I spent the winter months of 1939-40 on Achill Island supervising road construction, bridge construction and repairs to piers and boat slips on behalf of Mayo County Council. World War II was gaining momentum at the time and travel was becoming more difficult as cars, petrol, bicycles and spare parts were becoming more difficult to obtain. I can remember well my first 60 mile bicycle journey to Achill with a good stiff wind in my face. Between Mulranny and Achill, I caught up with a tramp locally known as Pateen. As I was making slow progress cycling against the strong wind, I decided to walk and enjoy his company to Achill. Observing some men digging around a telegraph pole, I told my companion that they must now be lifting up the line of telegraph poles, as the railway line had been closed down and the rails lifted a short time previously.

'Well indeed,' said the tramp, 'they could leave the poles alone because those poles were the only biteen of shelter they have in Achill.

Seeing me laugh at the idea of shelter from telegraph poles, the tramp said, 'I was fooled once when I was depending on those poles for shelter.'

Pointing to a densely populated village close to the old railway line, the tramp said, 'that village down there is Shruffaun and a nice friendly old crowd live down there. I seldom pass this way without calling down to see them. I can well remember being down there one cold stormy day a few years ago. A good friend of mine here in Tonragee gave me the tip and told me that my old friends down there would like me to call down to see them. The people of Shruffaun were enjoying a drink of poteen that came across from Ballycroy, and damn bad poteen it was. Anyhow I got more than my share of it. When I felt the drink was getting the better of me, I set off hoping to walk down the line to Mulranny as I had the wind on my back. As I got out on the railway line, I felt sick and drowsy. I looked up and saw three telegraph poles stuck together, so I decided to sit down in the shelter of the poles and rest. I must have gone to sleep right away. It must have been hours later when I awoke cold and shivering. When I looked up, I could only see one pole and I thought that one was falling over on top of me!'

We met a priest driving his car and I tried to sound Pateen as to his opinion of priests among his benefactors. 'Well,' he said, 'most of them are alright but I met some and they had as much charity in them as a storm out in Bunnafaughia.'

I was later to become acquainted with storms in this spot. Being perched on the Atlantic Drive high above the ocean and the nearest shelter in America (to quote a local saying), a storm there is no joke. The following year, I supervised the construction of sod fences around dangerous cliffs and coves in Bunnafaughia among other places in Achill. The sod fences were capped or crowned by heavy scraws six feet long and nearly a foot thick. Ten years later, I visited the Atlantic Drive with some tourists. I saw the scraws had been peeled off and big gaps blown through the wide sod fences by storms.

Getting back to my companion, he proceeded to tell me of a little brush, as he termed it, he had with a local parish priest. 'I remember,' he said, 'a few years ago I was caught by a big fall of snow down in Newport and could not get away for a week. When the thaw came, I was glad to be away so I called on my old friend Canon McDonnell as I knew he would not see me stuck for a bob or two. Fair enough, he handed me half-a-crown and said, 'I think you could be leaving now Pateen. I'm afraid the people are getting a little tired of your company.' 'Musha Father,' says I, 'isn't it a miserable little town that could not keep the two of us?'

Meeting an old man on the road, the tramp stood back to exchange a few words with him and then rejoined me with a broad smile. 'If you don't mind,' he said, 'that poor devil has got it in his head to get married.'

'I admire his courage,' said I.

'Courage,' scoffed the tramp, 'you could call it the *biseach chun báis*.' (This is an Achill saying meaning 'the improvement before death'.)

When I parted with my companion after a drink at Achill Sound, he said, 'we must soldier on to the end of the road, brother, and we should never worry too much about anything.' I really envied him the faculty of being able to look on life and its problems so lightly.

Around this time, the famous swing bridge at Achill Sound had been declared unfit to carry heavy traffic. One result of this was that two heavy stone crushing plants intended for road works in Achill by Mayo County Council could not travel to the island. All the broken stones required for road making in Achill had to be broken by hand with eight ounce hammers. The stones had to be broken small enough to pass through an iron ring three inches in diameter which was used occasionally for spot checks. Each man's pile of broken stone was shovelled through a wooden measure to determine tonnage. The pay rate was four shillings per ton of broken stone and the men were limited to three days' work per week. If a man had been in receipt of twelve shillings or over per week in unemployment assistance (dole), he could claim four days' work per week. To crown it all, the stone was a hard blue granite. All the bleakest and most windswept roads in Achill were staffed with stonebreakers when the scheme got under way. The Shraheen, Dooega, Keel-Dugort, Dooagh, and Bunnacurry Valley roads resembled British Empire building at its most pernicious in north west India as we read about it or saw it in pictures. One day I was sizing up the depressing sight of gangs of fine specimens of Irish manhood seated on piles of wet stones on the Shraheen road hammering away at the unrelenting granite and gneiss rocks. I was roused from my day dreams by the local parish priest. He told me he had called to know if there was any cursing by the workmen on the job.

'Oh yes Father,' I replied facetiously, 'the finest

cursing I ever heard in any part of the world.'

He told me that cursing was one of the worst sins and that I should not allow it. I replied that I was not so sure that it was a sin at all. I quoted the biblical passage about our Lord cursing the fig tree for not bearing fruit out of season.

'You must realise,' said the parish priest, 'that he was our Lord and he could do as he liked.'

I concluded by saying that apart from breaking the stones to size, the men could do as they liked as far as I was concerned. After the good Father departed, I began to wonder what reasons he would have given for all the cursing mentioned in *The Tripartite Life of Saint Patrick,* the cursing of Tara by St Ruadhan, or the litany of curses attributed to St Colmcille, who if we are to believe legend, must be the greatest fulminator of curses among all the Irish saints.

While residing at the foot of Tonragee mountain in 1938, I climbed the mountain one fine evening in spring. A companion, a local youth, gave me the history attached to a cairn of flagstones on the mountain summit, the cairn being known as 'Leachtaí Lytell'. Father Manus Sweeney, a native of Dookinella in the lower part of Achill Island, was executed in Newport on the day of the August Fair there in 1799 after a sham trial for complicity in the 1798 rebellion. His having been educated in France and having a good knowledge of the French language went a long way in securing his conviction with the judicial minions of English Imperialism, especially after the ill-fated French invasion of Mayo in the previous year. When Fr Manus mounted the scaffold, one of the onlookers was a native of the Protestant colony in Dugort, Achill, a man named Lytell who with two companions had attended the fair. Lytell, who had a fair knowledge of the Irish language and wanted to show his bigotry and hatred of priests, exclaimed, '*Tá splíonach shagairt ag éirí go hard inniu*'. (Priests' flesh is going high today.) A sister of Fr Manus who knew Lytell well (or according to another account, Fr Manus himself) turned to Lytell and told him not to be so brave or bold, that his own end would come some day and that he might not have so many witnesses to sympathise with him. Fr Manus was executed on the market crane in Newport, which stood on the market square up to twenty years ago. Executing political prisoners on fair days or occasions of public assembly was a ritual of the British calculated to strike terror into the greatest number of people. After the execution, Lytell and his two friends retired to a local alehouse and later set out on foot for home about twenty-eight miles away. As they approached the village of Tonragee a thick fog came in from Bellacraher Bay. The three travellers became separated in the fog. Two of them arrived in 'the colony' on the following day, but there was no trace of Lytell. Several days later, the dogs in Tonragee were observed coming down off the mountain carrying human bones in their descent. A search party followed them on their next journey up the mountain, found all that remained of Lytell and flung together the mound of stones to mark the spot. Having heard the tale, I wondered what unseen compelling force caused

Lytell to climb the steep side of Tonragee Mountain 1500 feet above Bellacraher Bay, and perish there alone.

WINDOW ON THE PAST

Before the Claremorris-Swinford-Collooney railway line was opened in 1895, Swinford for one hundred years had been a leading provincial market town for the sale of farm produce, chiefly butter, pigs and oats. The repeal of the corn laws around 1850 adversely affected oats production, so that afterwards the pig and the butter firkin became the small tenant's standby to meet his landlord's rent. The ford over the river at Mill Street, Swinford, was a mecca on fair mornings for hundreds of steaming pigs. Having been walked several miles to market they wallowed and washed themselves at this ford. Hence the name Swineford later shortened to Swinford.

In those days pigs were not sold until they were twelve months old. In summer when the previous year's potato crop ran out and before the new potato crop was harvested, they were often fed on green foods (cabbage, grass, coarse docks and other edible weeds), and were able to walk for miles to market. After a fair in Swinford, droves of pigs were walked to the ports of Ballina, Sligo and Newport. An old man told me he often saw scores of pigs being driven after the pig fairs in Swinford over the old Barnacoogue, Orlar, Carrowbehy route to Castlerea railway station.

The Swinford butter market attracted buyers from Sligo, Ballina, Westport, Newport and Killala and suppliers from all east Mayo and south Sligo. At one butter market in Swinford around 1880, a thousand firkins of butter were said to have been sold. As the gathering of one firkin of butter took months, this meant untold persevering, self-denial and drudgery for the housewife and her under-nourished family. At the market place, the butter buyers set up their tripod beam scales. Before being weighed or purchased, each firkin was pierced full length with an auger which when withdrawn showed if the butter was of uniform quality and colour. Prices were determined by this system of grading.

Afterwards local carters took the firkins to some port, usually Ballina or Sligo. The carter's lot was not an easy one. If listed for Sligo, a convoy of carts left Swinford about 5 a.m. Having delivered their loads at Sligo Quay, they collected a load of provisions to take back and tried to get to Ballinacarrow before nightfall where they stayed overnight. In bad weather, they felt lucky to get to Ballisodare on their way home. Between full and part-time carters, about fifty found employment in this way. Bunyan in his *Pilgrim's Progress* describes Vanity Fair as a seductive mart where all the wares of the world were bawled out to hoodwink poor Christian and make him tarry or turn aside from his pilgrimage. Swinford market was just as thronged and miscellaneous. The spacious Main Street square was packed with tradesmen, handymen and pedlars of all kinds displaying their wares. Coopers were there with tubs, firkins, piggins, noggins and churns; nailers with hand wrought nails; tinsmiths with tin cans, saucepans and tinker's lamps. This last named item was a gloveless paraffin oil burning contraption, giving off smoke and smell out of all proportion to the sickly light produced. Nevertheless, with paraffin oil selling for a halfpenny a pint, it gradually replaced dip candles and bog deal 'splits' for domestic lighting.

At the market, tailors were on hand to measure you for a suit of home spun frieze. As the art of packing footwear with cardboard had not arrived, cobblers measured your feet if required for a pair of comfortable boots guaranteed to give two years of 'honest wear'. As late as 1941, I saw this custom in operation at the fair in Achill Sound.

At Swinford market in those days, there were spinning wheels, wheel and hand-barrows, carts and cart-wheels, chairs, stools and a straw woven arm-chair called a *suísteog*. Upholstered with horse-hair or wool chippings, it was regarded as a luxury. Bundles of heather besoms neatly tied and trimmed were carried on the back from mountain districts and sold for a halfpenny each. Maxwell in his *Wild Sports of the West* asserted that on a market day in Tuam the number of beggars would outnumber the *lazzaroni* of Naples. In those days, in this respect, Swinford was little if any behind Tuam. After the Napoleonic and Crimean wars, every garrison town in Ireland had its quota of ex-soldiers. These – left without means of livelihood by their former masters – crowded into alleys and back streets like the Lane in Swinford or *Bóthar Garbh* in Claremorris. There they created social problems that remained down to recent years. In those days, there were knights of the road converging on the workhouses, ballad singers, travelling musicians and many other types of unfortunates. Petty robberies were a regular occurrence so that buyers and sellers strained a point to be clear of woods and 'heel of the town' spots before dark. Then, as now, there was the gap between the 'haves' and the 'have-nots'. Gombeen men as odious as the publicans of the Bible grew fat by lending money. Crocks of yellow sovereigns were displayed on some shop windows in Swinford during and for many years after the Famine, with the rate of interest and an exhortation to borrow displayed alongside. The interest rate of 5d per £1 seemed innocuous till the victim learned too late that this quotation meant 5d per month, or 25% annually. Happily this tribe of gombeen men have disappeared: 'nor left a wrack behind'.

These jottings are a window on the hard times that prevailed in Swinford and similar provincial market towns over the greater part of the last century.

THE NIGHT OF THE BIG WIND

The most disastrous and terror inspiring natural event in Irish history from 1798 to the Famine was the storm that swept the country on the night of Sunday, 6 January, and the morning of 7 January, 1839. It is believed that over seventy people were killed or drowned and well over one hundred more died from exposure and hardships attributable to the storm. Thousands were rendered homeless, boats were swamped or blown inland to incredible distances and smashed to matchwood and coaches were blown off the roads.

One group of Erris fishermen did not put to sea on that fateful night because, as they stoutly maintained later, they saw the *sí gaoithe* or storm spirit, a skeleton-like shadow with wildly waving arms silhouetted against a bank of sea fog.

Much of the destruction caused by the storm could have been avoided if the landlords had been more considerate towards their tenants. The tenants' dwellings would have in general been in better repair to withstand the storm but that every little improvement they carried out on their dwellings or farm buildings drew a reprisal from the landlord in the shape of an increase in their rent. In those days, petty country squires known as middlemen rented sections of the landlord's property which they then sublet to tenants. When a tenant tried to improve or shelter his home, the middleman reported the matter to the landlord who was not slow in increasing the tenant's rent to the mutual benefit of himself and the middleman.

An old song to the memory of the executed '98 leader Captain O'Malley of Eden, Knock, County Mayo, gives an idea of the plain people's hatred of the middlemen in the lines:

Mo mhallacht ar an mBrúnach, Mark Grady is a chomphlacht,
Na Diolúnaí is Diucaí 's na Daibhisí breána fós,
Sé ár mallacht 's ar sciúirse ó Swinford go Cúl Luachra.
Ó Scrig go Tullaí Luachra na middlemen agus Yeos

An Brúnach was the notorious County Sheriff (Donncha an Rópa) of Claremount House, Claremorris. Mark Grady, Dukes, Dillons and Davis were militia officers or middlemen under his regime.

Some days after the big storm, a son of Donncha an Rópa was inspecting his property along the Claremorris-Balla road. He saw one of his tenant's houses from which the apex stone on the gable was missing. This stone, known in Gaelic as the *cloch phréacháin,* had been blown down by the big storm. Landlord Browne informed the tenant that he was increasing his rent by five shillings for not replacing the stone and repairing the gable.

We may take the town of Swinford as an example of the terrible damage wrought in small towns throughout the country by the storm. Blowing from the north-west, the storm of 1839 caught Swinford on its exposed side, there being no railway station or sheltering railroad embankments at the time. Piles of thatch, slates, timbers and roofing flagstones blocked the streets. One street, Mill Street, was left without a single roof which had not been blown down. In its humble way, Mill Street was then the industrial sector of Swinford. Nailers, coopers, shoemakers, weavers, tailors and tinsmiths worked side by side in houses that have since disappeared.

One young man in Ballydrum village was so worried about his two stacks of oats, his only standby to pay his landlord's rent, that he got a ladder and climbed on to one stack and stayed there all through the storm to keep the stack from being blown away. His widowed mother climbed on to the other stack and did likewise. During the night, one fierce gust of wind swept her shawl away and it was found in Killaturly, two miles away. It was recognised by a large shawl safety pin which was a new innovation at the time. The shawl pin had been given to the old woman by the lady at the Big House as a gift for paying her rent so promptly. The pin's being fastened caused the shawl to balloon and be carried so far by the storm. The threshing flail had only been introduced to the village a short time before the storm and before then the scutching stone was an important part of farm equipment. The old woman who lost her shawl said that the storm must have been sent as a punishment for adopting such a devil's emblem as the flail.

When the Old Age Pensions Act granting pensions at the age of seventy became law in 1909, anyone born on or before the night of The Big Wind automatically qualified for a pension. As no records of births or deaths were kept in 1839 or for many years afterwards, claimants had to appear before a pensions official, magistrate or clergyman and satisfy him as to the genuineness of their claims. Many children born around the time of the great storm had been told by their mothers that they were born on the 'night of the Big Wind'. The result was that the number claiming to have been born on that night reached a staggering total.

One parish priest in a parish near Swinford appointed a certain day on which to take particulars from pension claimants. When he found almost all the claimants saying that they were born on the night of the Big Wind, he exclaimed, 'It must have been the greatest storm since the beginning of the world if it blew you all into the world on the same night.'

One applicant from Swinford district told the pensions officer that he well remembered the night of the Big Wind. Asked what he remembered about it, he said, 'I remember my mother blessing herself and shoving me and my cradle under the bed and saying the house would fall on us.'

'Surely,' said the pensions officer, 'you don't expect me to believe that you remember what happened when you were in the cradle.'

The old man told him that he was the youngest

member of his family and that in his day the youngest child might have to sleep in the cradle for years owing to shortage of accommodation. He told the official that cradles were often made outsize on that account. The pensions officer smilingly allowed his claim.

With modern buildings, more staunch and better sheltered farmsteads and advance warnings of gales being announced, it seems unlikely that the havoc and terror caused by the storm of 1839 can be repeated in this country.

WAKING THE GAEL

Many theories have been advanced to explain the old Gaelic custom of playing games at wakes for the dead. All authorities agree that no disrespect for the dead was intended. Very often relatives of a deceased person asked the younger people at the wake to commence the games. Often an old man, feeling his end draw near, gave instructions as to the games to be indulged in at his wake.

The old Gaelic race looked on a natural death as a happy release from the cares and worries of this world to a happier life in the next world. Only when a young person met a sudden or untimely end did they regard it as a cause for lamentation. Down to recent years, when the last sod of turf was cut, the last sheaf of grain reaped or some other seasonal work completed, God's mercy on the dead was invariably invoked by the people involved in the work. When enjoying the first sample of some fruit or vegetable such as new potatoes, the usual saying was, '*Go mbeirimid beo ag an am seo arís* – that we may be alive this time again' (next year). I have often heard those invocations which prove that consideration for the dead and thoughts of the hereafter were never far from the mind of the Gael. East Mayo seems to have been one of the last strongholds in Ireland of the custom of playing games at wakes as there are many people still alive who took part in them. The First World War and the troubled times helped to put an end to many old world ideas. Some of those games were just trials of strength or agility, such as 'tug-of-war' with a brush handle over a chalked line on the floor or jumping over and back across a stick while holding an end in each hand.

Two of the most popular games were known as *Thart an Bhróg* and Riding the Blind Donkey. In the first named game, a number of players sat in a circle and secretly passed some small object to each other. A 'victim' seated on a chair in the centre of the circle was expected to name correctly who was in possession of the object when asked. The object was often a child's shoe and to mislead the man in the middle the person in possession of the shoe would whisper '*cuir thart an bhróg*' (pass the shoe). This is how the game got its name.

In the game of Riding the Blind Donkey two stout kitchen chairs were placed about four feet apart. A strong spade or shovel handle was placed horizontally with an end resting on the seat of each chair. The operator then had to sit cross-legged like a tailor on the spade handle. While precariously balanced there, four small objects such as potatoes or small sods of turf were placed on the outer corners of the chair seats and he was expected to knock those objects on to the floor with a short stick while maintaining his balance. The penalties or forfeits for failure in those games varied in different localities. The penalty in *Thart* was usually a number of 'thumps' on the back by the strong man of the company. As a concession, the victim might be allowed to hold his open hand palm outwards on his back to cushion the blows. In other places, the punishment might be a number of blows of a knotted straw rope. In Riding the Blind Donkey the punishment often was to force a handful of *deannach* down the fallen jockey's back between shirt and skin. *Deannach* was a dusty abrasive product of oat milling, and as small oat mills dotted the countryside in those days, there was no shortage of the commodity. It had the property of generating a most unbearable itch on tender skin. Near Claremorris a small lake bears the name of *Loch na nDeannach* owing to the *deannach* formerly dumped there.

An old man in south Mayo once told me of a game played at wakes around Claremorris in his youth. This game, which could hardly be called a parlour game, was known as *Bearradoir* (the shaver). A number of young men lined up to be shaved, each being compelled to take a large mouthful of water and stand with distended cheeks while the barber or shaver gave him a mock shave with a goose or duck quill while intoning the words, *'Bearrfaidh mise mo sheandhuinín go lom, lom, lom.'* This implied that he would shave his client bare, bare, bare. If any client laughed, the rest squirted their mouthful of water in his face. Sometimes the unfortunate barber was on the receiving end when his client's mouthful of water exploded in his face.

The playing of those games was not always confined to wakes. Sometimes they were played on the night after a *meitheal* assembled to help a backward neighbour with some seasonal work or when flax scutching or some such work was completed.

When the journeyman tailor came to a village, he usually billeted in some 'ready' house where there were no children to interfere with his work and where he often stayed the whole winter. Owing to the poor lighting facilities in those days it was work all day and play and yarns all night as people gathered to while away the long winter hours before bedtime. Years ago in the village of *Gleann Mhullaigh an Eo* (Charlestown) I heard fragments of a local song to commemorate the visit of a journeyman tailor Seán Bán Duffy and his apprentice Mullaney. One verse contained the lines:

There was cally for Mullaney and boxty for Seán Bán,
And with songs and tales and games galore we waited till the dawn.

(Cally was the equivalent of the English 'colcannon').

At funerals, which usually proceeded from the deceased's home in those days, all the neighbouring young men gathered in some field out of sight of the house of mourning. There for two or three strenuous hours they indulged in athletic feats: jumping, weight throwing and weight lifting, long and high jumping, wrestling, etc. There was a keen air of friendly rivalry between opposing townlands, and it was here records were reached or broken. Regular athletic or sports meetings were out of bounds in some areas as some landlords did not want land being cut up and trampled unduly by young men whom they described as 'skylarking vagabonds'.

BEFORE THE FAMINE

When the English writer and farming expert Arthur Young toured Ireland two hundred years ago, he was very critical of the wasteful farming methods he found there. Of course he should have directed his fire more to the landlord class who were mainly responsible. If a tenant tried to improve his farm or farm buildings, the landlord increased his rent and could evict him whenever he pleased. One of the few things that pleased Arthur Young was 'the view of Lough Key from the Rock of Doon' in north Roscommon. He classed it as the grandest scenery he had beheld in any part of the world. He appreciated the view all the more as he had been passing through plain uninteresting countryside when the view of Lough Key with its wooded islands and their historic ruins burst into view. For a similar reason, a traveller going through south-west Sligo between Tubbercurry and Ballina might feel enraptured when the view of Lough Talt comes into view. Before coming to the lake from either direction, the visitor passes through the plain featureless foothills of the Ox Mountains, described by a geologist who toured the area as 'uninteresting hills of gneiss and schist.'

Close to the lake lies the lonely glen of Glanavoo. The holy well there, known as St Attracta's well, was a popular place of pilgrimage in former times. At the north-western end of the lake a high well-built stone wall encloses 13,000 acres of rough mountainside. I had mistakenly taken this wall to be a boundary fence for one of the deer parks which were so common as part of a landlord's estate in times gone by until I learned that the wall and the ground enclosed by it were part of a land project initiated in 1839 by the Irish Waste Land Improvement Society. While the scheme was not over-ambitious, it was at least a beginning. Among its weak points, it was slanted more to the benefit of its shareholders than to the slaving occupants of the land; it still offered no security of tenure to the tenants. The Society in its preamble described its objectives as 'the provision of a liberal profit to the shareholders as well as providing employment to the industrious and necessitious peasantry.'

In 1839 the Society bought a bankrupt landlord's estate at Gleneask near Lough Talt in County Sligo. This landlord had impoverished the tenants as well as himself with rent increases. This short-sighted policy had backfired on him so much that the Society bought it cheaply. It was the last word in a run-down neglected estate. The Society, in leasing this land, stipulated that no lease should run beyond the life of a tenant. This in itself was a disincentive to the tenant to improve his holding. No lease was issued to the tenant with less than twenty Irish acres. Those with less than twenty acres were classed as tenants-at-will, meaning they had no claim on their holdings beyond day to day occupation. This maintained a high percentage of the tenants, over forty families in all, at the level of peons or squatters.

Main drains were to be constructed at the Society's expense, while the tenants were to make cross drains and surface drains. Thirty miles of roads were built by the Society. New houses were built to replace the houses of the tenants which were described as being with a few exceptions 'badly built, damp, and wretched'. The Society undertook to build cottages thirty feet long, twelve to fourteen wide and eight to ten feet high, of stone or brick, with roof of slate or thatch, at a cost to the tenants of £20 for each house.

Each holder was to have one or more cows, with an expected return of seventy-five to one hundred and twelve pounds of butter annually. This butter was expected to fetch 8d per pound in the Sligo butter market. If sold in the more convenient Swinford butter market, the price averaged ½d per pound less, and at that time every ½d counted. The people's main food was potatoes and buttermilk. Labourers working for the Society were paid 10d per day without food or 8d per day if a meal was provided. This was the summer rate for a twelve hour day; 2d per day less was paid for a nine hour day in winter.

The Society placed emphasis on livestock rearing in preference to increased tillage. They claimed that increased livestock rearing would mean more fodder production and eventually more farmyard manure to enrich the land. Only a low percentage of the land could be classed as arable. Some of the cottages were roofed with slate quarried in nearby Mount Taafe. Unfortunately the slate deposits were too inaccessible to encourage worthwhile production. The Waste Land Improvement Society bought a second impoverished landlord's estate at Ballinakill in north Connemara around the same time as their purchase of the Gleneask estate. They proceeded to develop both estates on similar lines.

Unfortunately, when they felt that they were making headway to the 'mutual benefit of their tenants and shareholders', the Great Famine of 1847 struck with full force. It resulted in two-thirds of the Society's tenants ending in famine graves or on emigrant ships and the collapse of the Land Improvement Schemes. To make matters worse, the tenants had grown more potatoes than usual. When the potato blight struck with full force, it wiped out their promising potato crop in a few days. The summer of 1847 was the wettest in living memory, and with the stalks blighted the tubers, in the words of a local man, 'stood no stagger' but rotted steadily in the sodden heavy clay. There had been local outbreaks of potato blight in 1845 and 1846, but with the continuous rain in 1847 the outbreak was nationwide. There were warnings sounded by farming experts and public bodies in '45 and '46 but the government of the day callously ignored all of them.

MOUNTAIN DEW

North and east Mayo, in common with other parts of Ireland where the distillation of poteen or illicit whiskey was routine, had their legendary characters who were noted for the good quality of their product or for their resourcefulness in thwarting or evading the law. Over one hundred years ago one of the best known poteen makers in Mayo was a man known as Red Owen Judge. He lived on a slope of the Ox Mountains a few miles from Foxford. One day he set out for Foxford with a donkey carrying two creels of turf for sale. The creels were wicker work or woven rod baskets suspended across the donkey's back. Under the turf in one creel was a gallon jar of poteen. Owen Judge heard that a new police sergeant (R.I.C.) had been appointed to Foxford and he was anxious to sell as much poteen as possible before making his acquaintance. He had learned from another home brew expert in Sligo that the new sergeant was a good judge of a right drop and came down more heavily on those making bad stuff. As he came within a half mile of Foxford, he met the sergeant walking along leisurely. The sergeant of course had found a description of Owen and others of the same profession in the barracks, so he guessed he had the right man for an interview. He casually held up Owen, and after a few words about the quality and price of the turf, he lifted a few sods and found the jar. Owen betrayed no dismay but asked him if he was the new sergeant. When the sergeant answered that he was, Owen told him that the jar contained a special good drop that he was taking in to him because, said Owen, 'I heard a man from your last station in Sligo to say that you were a good judge of real good stuff.'

After some consideration, the sergeant said, 'Well, in that case, carry on to Foxford and call to my house and leave the turf there as well as the jar. There is another jar there and cover the two jars well with the turf. Tell my wife I sent you, and God help you if your stuff is not as good as what is in the other jar,' added the sergeant with a smile.

Owen continued his journey to Foxford and went at once to the sergeant's house. He told the sergeant's wife that he was in a hurry and to hand him out the jar that was in the turf shed. 'Your husband is expecting a call this evening from the D.I. (District Inspector) and he does not like to have any poteen lying around when that man calls.'

'I do not blame him for that,' added Owen, 'as the same D.I. would smell poteen a mile away.'

The sergeant's wife handed out the jar and Owen lost no time in taking it to the other end of the town and selling it along with his own jar. Knowing that the sergeant was trying night and day to get him, Owen had to lie low and be more vigilant than ever. For a year or more, he made his whiskey in remote hideouts and got other people who were not suspect to sell it for him. After a year of caution, Owen decided to take a chance and run a round at home on Christmas Eve. When he got his plant set up and everything humming, he strolled out to his lookout spot. He had a good pair of field glasses with him that he had brought with him from England in his youth.

When he focused his glasses on the road to Foxford, he was horrified to see the sergeant and two comrades less than a mile away on foot and heading in his direction. He rushed indoors and dragged the still, worm, cooler, etc., into the bedroom. He then took the large fire and took it into two neighbours' houses that were side by side with his own. Hastily disrobing, he got into the hag bed, as most kitchen beds were then called. He told his wife to call in the children and say he had just died. She did that and then she called in the woman next door to assist. She was also a Mrs Judge and was a professional crier. Criers were women who attended all wakes and funerals and cried and lamented, chanted the praises of the deceased and clapped their hands in paroxysms of grief. In many instances criers did not know (nor care) who the deceased was.

The sergeant and his men arrived just as the two women, having hung a set of white curtains outside the bed and placing a lighted candle on a chair beside the bed, were getting into their stride crying as well as Owen's children who really believed that he had died. When Owen's wife, between sobs, told the sergeant of Owen's demise, he turned to his men and ordered a retreat, saying under his breath, 'too bad he did not do this a year ago.' Some days later the sergeant learned the true story. He at once applied for a transfer, stating that he felt the poteen menance was well under control in his area.

Another noted distiller who flourished in the same area a generation later was known as the Legger. He earned the title from his prowess in escaping on foot from his pursuers whenever they tried to surprise him at his distillery. His would-be captors guessed his identity from his long legs and massive strides, but could never get close enough to positively identify him. Finding himself under extra security and with no income in sight, he wrote a brief note to the sergeant in Foxford, ostensibly as a tip-off. The note stated that the Legger would be taking a donkey cart load of turf to Foxford the next Saturday morning and that he would have a two gallon jar of poteen hidden in the turf.

Delighted with the tip, the sergeant met the Legger on the outskirts of the town and told him he just wanted a load of turf. When he asked what the price would be, the Legger said five shillings. The sergeant felt that in the circumstances it was worth the difference, so he told the Legger to take it around to his place and he would show him where to dump it. The Legger innocently asked him would the next load suit as he had another customer waiting for turf.

'No,' said the sergeant, 'and here is your five shillings and get a move on, I can't be waiting all day.'

The Legger took the load around and emptied it under the vigilant eye of the sergeant, who found that he had got the nicest turf 'from Pollagh Bog to Knockfadda', to quote the Legger's own words.

I can remember an old woman of eighty from Killasser parish telling of the adventures of her father in the poteen making industry. 'My father, grandfather and great-grandfather,' she said, 'all had the name of making first class whiskey. If a round did not turn out good as they expected, they would dump it rather than give their stuff a bad name. On one occasion, my father got an order for two gallons from the parish priest in Kiltimagh. We had a young half-trained horse at the time. I was a young schoolgirl, but being the oldest of the family, my father took me with him partly to help with the horse and partly to attract less notice to our real business. He put the jar of whiskey in the cart and put a bag of hay over it. He told me to sit on the box and keep a firm hold of the horse's reins. He took a short hold of the horse's bridle and walked by his head all the way to Kiltimagh, eleven or twelve miles away.

'When we got to Kiltimagh, we found it was fair day there. When our horse saw all the cattle on the street, he began to prance and back away from them. The police barracks at that time was close by and the sergeant was standing outside. When he saw our trouble, he walked over and spoke to the horse and patted him. He then took a hold of the horse's bridle on the opposite side to my father. In that way, the horse gave no more trouble. When we got to the parish priest's gate, the sergeant turned back, giving me a slow wink as he did so. I heard afterwards that he was one of those who attended small parties in the priest's house sometimes. I have no doubt that he guessed who we were and had a good idea of our reason for going to the parish priest's house.

'My father always believed in leaving a drop outside for the good people [fairies] any night that he made a round. Any night he forgot this, he regretted it as that round would go against him. He always made sure to put the *braon broghach* aside by itself to use as a rub for rhumatism, and a good cure it always was. Many a time it was a help to myself,' she concluded.

The *braon broghach*, pronounced 'breen broagh', was the first two cupfuls of the round that came from the still. As its name implies, it tasted bitter but had its commercial value as a liniment.

IN FEUDAL DAYS

During the famine years 1845-49, many Mayo landlords, finding further evictions unprofitable and further increases in rackrents impossible, initiated instead a system of forced labour. Tenants were forced to report to their landlord and work gratuitously, according to the size of their rents: cultivating and reclaiming 'his honour's' lands, levelling buildings, garden walls, etc., of evicted tenants and other 'useful' works. Their reward was one meal daily for a working day of twelve hours.

One landlord in Killasser parish solved the problem of feeding his workers by driving out to them in his horse and cart with a tub of stirabout (Indian meal porridge). His son was heckled about it in later times at an election meeting in Swinford. Years ago I heard an old man from Carracastle parish tell of his grandfather working for a similar reward for his landlord, Phillips of Cloonmore. As the potato famine eased, the Cloonmore landlord changed the meal of porridge to a ration of potatoes which the workers roasted in an open fire. This was termed a 'cast' of potatoes. As times improved and herrings got cheaper, a cooked salty herrying wrapped in a cabbage leaf was occasionally sent out to each worker in addition to his potato 'cast'.

At Hagfield House, nearby dinner was served to the workers in the yard on a shovel. On one occasion, the Cloonmore slaves were busy digging out their landlord's potatoes alongside the Carracastle-Doocastle road. Around noon a petty landlord Joe Mór McDonnell of Doocastle emerged from the Big House leading an old nag after an all night party with their landlord. Joe Mór complained to the starving workers that 'Tomeen Phillips's geese were tough as leather,' and that after drinking four bottles of his wine and four of his whiskey he was still going home sober. He was known all over Mayo as the Doocastle Sunday Man, not for religious fervour but because Sunday was the only day of the week he could claim immunity from arrest by his creditors if he left his own grounds.

Joe's other claim to fame rested on his great size and phenomenal appetite. He sat as an M.P. for Mayo in the House of Commons after he gained victory over George Henry Moore of Moorehall with the aid of Archbishop McHale and the clergy in the famous 1847 election. Moore had enlightened national views and treated his famine stricken tenants with more humanity than any landlord in Mayo. Joe Mór's term in the Commons was short, as he was ousted by Moore the following year. During the 1848 election, it leaked out that Joe Mór was not averse to a good meat dinner on Fridays and he was severely heckled about this at a meeting in Foxford. When the heckling began he took a letter from his pocket, offered a bet of £20 that it was in the handwriting of Pope Pius IX and then read, 'My dear Joe. I am glad to hear that you are carrying on the fight for the ould faith in

County Mayo. As a mark of my appreciation for your zeal and hard work, you are not to fast or abstain until the campaign is over. Yours truly, Pius IX.'

Their wits dulled by famine and oppression, many believed the huge fraud. In offering a bet of £20, he was on safe ground as possibly his listeners had not £20 among them (and neither had Joe).

In 1847 the opposition leader in the House of Commons Lord Bentinck sponsored a motion to allot eighteen million pounds for famine relief work in Ireland. Fearing another election, Joe Mór and another Mayo M.P. Dillon Browne of Glencorrib voted with the government and helped to defeat the motion. At the time, some of McDonnell's neighbours were dying on their way to Swinford workhouse. Others were dying from surfeits of spawned salmon or trout, the toxic effects of which in their run-down condition they were unable to withstand. As the rivers and fish belonged to the landlords, this was a hush-hush matter. It should be noted that Gavan Duffy in his memoirs referred to Dillon Browne as 'the worst type of an Irish place hunter'.

One of the most influential landlord families in east Mayo in those days were the Ormsbys of Ballinamore. Thomas Ormsby sat on the jury that sent Fighting Fitzgerald to the gallows in 1796. Three years later, he filled a similar role when Fr Conroy, the patriot priest of Addergoole, was sentenced to death in Castlebar. Over the lean post-famine years, his son Black Anthony Ormsby ruled in Ballinamore with the traditional severity of his ancestors towards his tenants. Yet he found one tenant pliable enough to compose a lengthy poem in praise of Ballinamore and its landlord. Despite the poet's lavish praise, only one line of the poem pleased Ormsby. 'I'm sure it's as strong as the Temple of Rome', comparing the Big House of course with the Vatican. The nicely wooded Ballinamore demesne, watered by the winding Yellow River and overshadowed by Sliabh Chairna or Slievehorn, one of the hills in Ireland to be inhabited and cultivated above an attitude of eight hundred feet, is a pleasing spot. Yet the author of the Ballinamore planxty was keeping well up to the Irish peasant poet's love of exaggeration when he wrote:

This place so delighting 'tis also enticing,
I'm sure that its equal was ne'er seen before.
For the nobles of Dublin drive down in their
coaches
To view that grand place called Ballinamore.

Another poem, *The Whiskers of Ballinamore* was not so complimentary. It tells of a rent collection day in Ballinamore when Black Anthony ordered three tenants from his presence because they had grown whiskers, as he thought in imitation of his own flowing black beard. He ordered:

Get off those whiskers and that without delay,
Or fifteen shillings yearly, with your rent you all
must pay.

As refusal meant eviction the tenants complied

with his demand. In his opening lines the poet sang,

In the Parish of Killedan in the County of Mayo,
There dwells a cruel landlord whose name I'll let you know.
There rules a cruel landlord whose tenants suffer sore,
And they call him Tony Ormsby the Lord of Ballinamore.

Having sent all landlords to warm regions the poet concludes:

Now all you weary bachelors and rambling boys take care,
If you happen to be tempted a whisker for to wear.
Be wary of your landlord now and for evermore,
Or else he might mistreat you like the Boy from Ballinamore.

THE FRIAR'S CHRISTMAS NIGHT

It was a cold dark Christmas night in 1847, the peak year of the terrible famine. An aged friar, the last of the Carmelite Friars from the now dying but once influential friary of Ballinsmall, two miles east of Claremorris, was hurrying on foot on the road from Claremorris to Knock. He was going in answer to a sick call to the village of Dalton about four miles north of Ballinsmall. He was accompanied by his neighbour and part-time servant Mark Gabhlain (or Forkan). Although their road was a Grand Jury road, as main trunk roads were then called, and was the road used by the Bianconi coaches plying between Sligo and Galway, it was rutted and dangerous after dark. On that account, they had to travel slowly in places and the friar's companion carried a military style lantern. This was something of a novelty as the only torches used by peasants in those days were live coals impaled on iron spikes or old reaping hooks.

A well known sheebeen stood at the junction of their road and another very old road at Barnacarroll. This other road was one of the roads that formed part of the Tochar Phadraig or pilgrim road that took pilgrims to Croaghpatrick. It was also an important road linking the old castles of Ballyhowley, Murneen and Brize. The forces of General Lake travelled over it in 1798 to retake Castlebar from the United Irishmen. On passing the sheebeen holding his lantern low to the ground, Mark Gabhlain observed two unusually bright-looking crowns close to the grass margin. Mark Gabhlain felt that the money was a Heaven-sent gift and that they should avail of it to get a tumbler or two of punch to help them on their way. In those days, the steaming bowl of whiskey punch was a popular remedy among the peasantry for most human ills. Nearly everybody had faith in a bowl of punch in its own good time, and in this regard, the friar was no exception.

The good friar hesitated, but only for a moment. He then bade his man to cover the crowns with two small flagstones from the road fence. 'If they are there, 'he said, 'on our return, well and good.'

The friar arrived at his destination just in time and with not a minute to spare to anoint a young man who lay dying. He waited till all was over and the Rosary recited for the deceased before setting out on his return journey with his companion. He felt happy and kept thanking God that he had not yielded to temptation when passing the sheebeen, while Mark Gabhlain allowed himself visions of steaming punch when they got back to the sheebeen. When they got to the spot where they has seen the crowns, they found the flagstones undisturbed, to Mark's joy. He hastily lifted the stones. All he found was a large black *ciaróg* (cockroach) under each stone. . .

THE MOY CORRIES

Up to the drainage of the River Moy in the late 1950s and early 1960s, forecasting weather conditions with the aid of the stepping stones, or corries as they were locally called, was a time honoured custom. (In some districts the lines of stepping stones were called *clochâns*.) In calm weather, old people living within a mile of the river could predict with uncanny accuracy if a change in weather conditions was imminent or if existing weather was to continue by listening, usually before retiring at night, to the changing sounds of the water passing through the corries. In my neighbourhood, if Cloonacanana corrie sounded loudest, it foretold rain. If Seán's corrie was the noisiest it meant frost in winter or colder than average weather in summer. If Cruckawn-Aughanna corrie was 'going', to use a local term, it meant fine weather. When atmospheric conditions, anti-cyclones, wind direction and other such reasons were given to account for the behaviour of the corries, the older people scoffed at those ideas. They had their own legends and traditions and stuck to them until the drag lines lifted all the corries and broke a grand link with the past. In 1947 I can remember Seán's corrie being as noisy as an express train night and day for some days before the onset of a record breaking frost spell which lasted for five weeks and culminated in a blizzard of drifting snow which brought all wheeled traffic in the country to a standstill.

With the possible exception of the earthen forts which abound in this part of the country, no other physical feature of the countryside carried such a wealth of folklore and *pisreógs* as the corries. The round towers, being of pre-Christian origin, also carry a wealth of pagan folklore. (It seems strange that some learned authorities regard the round towers as being of Christian origin without a single shred of evidence, not even an etched cross which should be the hallmark of Christianity, to support their beliefs.)

Seán's corrie was named after a famous Killasser poteen-maker who flourished two hundred years ago named Seán Ó Ruadhain. On one occasion, he was escaping across the corrie named after him with a jar of poteen, closely pursued by the revenue men. Seeing more revenue men on the opposite bank, Seán smashed the jar on the stepping stone at his feet. Not to be outdone, the revenue men went downstream along the river to Cloonacanana corrie. There they recovered the poteen-soaked cork and convicted Seán on that piece of flimsy evidence. Being a native of a rebellious inclination, he had no chance of an acquittal. During Black and Tan days, many men on the run used the corries to escape dragnets and encircling operations.

ULTACHS

In my youth, I often heard the name Ultach added to some people's names to distinguish them from persons with similar surnames. I still hear this title applied, but not so frequently. On inquiring the reason, I found that the Ultachs, meaning Ulster people, were descendants of the victims of Protestant bigotry and persecution who had to flee from Ulster, in some cases as far back as 1793. Around that time, a secret Protestant society was formed in north-east Ulster with the avowed object of banishing all Catholics to 'Hell or to Connacht', a statement which was a revival of Oliver Cromwell's proclamation of over one hundred and fifty years earlier. This secret society, because they carried out their acts of murder, arson and intimidation at daybreak, took the title of 'Peep O' Day Boys'. This society, after 1795 changing its name to the 'Orange Society' or 'Orangemen', earned and is still earning worldwide notoriety as the ultimate in religious bigotry and intolerance. In 1795 a convention of Ulster magistrates and lawmakers, presided over by Lord Gosford, Governor of Armagh, condemned the Orange Society as a lawless banditti guilty of dreadful murders and destruction of property. All but one member of this convention were Protestants. Despite this, the religious persecution continued unabated. Catholics who got the customary twelve hour's notice to get out were in one respect the lucky ones, as many were shot out and burned out (to quote an Orange Society report) without warning. A society known as the 'Defenders' sprang up to defend Catholic property, but with obsolete arms, they had little hope of turning the tables on their well armed opponents. Most of the refugees who fled to County Mayo because of this persecution came from County Armagh. Tiernans of Foxford and Louisburgh, a number of Dunleavys and Conveys in Killasser parish, the O'Neills of Newcastle, Meelick (Swinford) and some of the Keanes, Heaneys and Morleys in east Mayo are among others descended from those who had to flee before the Orange terror. Sometimes those people who fled had to gather their livestock, poultry and other belongings and head for Connacht in the depths of winter. The Orangemen took extra delight in intensifying their campaign in winter. The journey to west Connacht sometimes lasted up to eight weeks, depending on weather conditions and the assistance or opposition they encountered on the way. Luckily for themselves, they came at a time when Mayo landlords were looking for tenants, as they had many vacant holdings on their lands. Emigration, chiefly to the United States and Canada, was getting into full swing and whole families were leaving from Mayo every week. Many more holdings were vacant through the wholesale eviction policy of the more tyrannical of the landlords. The Ultachs brought advanced farming ideas with them to Connacht.

One of my informants said that even to catch a salmon, snare a trout or hare or make a good drop of mountain dew, they were hard to beat. One man of the Ultach posterity told me that he fully believed that his grandfather made the best poteen in Ireland. He pointed to a small moss covered ruin between fifty and a hundred yards from his dwelling house and said, 'My grandfather was born and reared there.'

'Some time,' he continued, 'after my grandfather's parents died and his sisters had gone to America, he felt it was time to think of getting married. He decided to make a run of poteen as a first step. When he had all ready for firing, he got two neighbours to help him. He was getting a good return. He had very few bottles in hand, so he had almost every spare vessel in the house filled with poteen. Some time after midnight, they all seemed to get weak with hunger, and taking sips of the whiskey only made them worse, so my grandfather said he would cook something to eat. Two or three days before, a good calf belonging to one of his neighbours broke a leg and had to be killed and salted. The owner sent in a large lump of veal to my grandfather. In those days if a neighbour had only one potato, he would share it with another neighbour if he was in need of it. Today they would hardly give you the *cuasán*. [The *cuasán* was a vacant space or vacuum at the core of the potato, sometimes equal to the size of a large marble. It seems something was lacking in the growth and formation of the potato which retarded the completion of its programe. I have not seen a *cuasán* (pronounced coosaun) in a potato over the past fifty years. Possibly the use of more fertilisers has helped the potato to close the gap.] In those days, most of the heifer calves were sold to butchers for killing to keep down the cattle population.

'My grandfather put the veal in a small pot or skillet and hung it over the fire but it seems he put the veal in the wrong pot. He had the first dash of poteen, called the *braon broghach* (ugly drop) in one pot. It was as inflammable as paraffin oil. Before they noticed anything the chimney was blazing and then the thatch. My grandfather had barely enough time to grab his best clothes and whatever money was in the house and get out before the house all went up on fire.

'When the neighbours gathered the next day to thatch the house again my grandfather said he would wait a day or two. He felt that the house was too near the old fairy fort at the back and he never seemed to have much luck in it. He went to a wise woman who lived above the town of Swinford, Bid Heaney, and when she came, she pointed out this spot instead for building the house on. My grandfather did as she told him and found he had better luck after that.'

OLD CHARMS AND CUSTOMS

Superstitious and semi-superstitious customs and charms were to a large extent a feature of rural life in Ireland up to and including the famine years. As whole villages were wiped out by the famine or by the succeeding mass evictions by rackrenting landlords, many old traditions and customs disappeared forever. But some of the old customs lingered on even down to our own time.

A charm or cure that seemed to be popular in south Mayo down to a couple of generations ago was Crean's or Creheen's blood; this meant blood belonging to anybody by the name of Crean, locally pronounced Creheen. It was believed that a few drops were an infallible cure for lung or chest ailments if the blood was diluted with hot water and the vapour inhaled by the affected person.

I can recall being told in my school days by an old man of a trip made by him to an old woman of the Crean clan for the 'cure' for his grandmother who was 'caught up in the chest'. The old woman with the Crean surname simply tied her index finger at two points near the tip and base, made a small gash on her finger between the two points and gave him the required blood. The man's grandmother said she felt a big improvement having tried the remedy. The blood donor took no cash in payment but accepted two ounces of tobacco and a naggin of whiskey as a gift.

I remember in my younger days listening to an old man, Ned Flanagan telling of a trip he once made to 'the far end of Kilmovee parish' on behalf of his young wife who got a dust or hayseed in her eye while haymaking. His trip was to an old woman who possessed cure for disorders of the eyes. According to Ned Flanagan, this old woman on hearing his story got a saucer of spring water, made the sign of the cross over it and said what he believed to be a prayer in a low voice. She then called over Ned and showed him the cause of his wife's trouble, a small hayseed which had begun to sprout. Having left a small bottle of whiskey as a present to the old woman, Ned Flanagan set out on the sixteen mile walk to his home. On his arrival, his wife informed him that she got instant relief in the affected eye around three o'clock in the afternoon, which was around the time Ned was shown the hayseed floating in the saucer of water.

The use of sprain threads, measuring the head, charms for ringworm and other minor ailments are still practised in parts of rural Ireland. I can remember seeing a partly disabled old man Paddy McCann 'measuring the head' for victims of headache or dizziness. His technique was to loop a string around the sufferer's head while murmuring what I took to be a prayer in a low indistinct voice. His payment or gift was usually 'a half quarter' (two ounces) of tobacco. To cure boils, carbuncles or external blemishes, bathing in water at a point where three parishes met (or better still four parishes) was recommended.

The thread to cure sprains was confined to, and handed down in, certain families. If an old man or woman possessing the sprain thread had no family or if all his family had emigrated, the thread was handed down to a niece, nephew or some other close relation. When any sufferer had occasion to send for the sprain thread, the messenger was instructed to go 'around the road', as taking a short cut through fields was believed to lessen the speedy efficacy of the charm.

If anybody was lucky enough to collect the dropping seeds of the Royal Fern (*Raithneach na Rí)* he was said in olden times to have a charm worth his weight in gold. One snag was that the seeds had to be collected at midnight on St John's Eve, a date to which a lot of old beliefs were linked. May Day (1 May) and Samhain Eve, the eve of 1 November, were also favourite dates for old ideas and customs. An object of mixed fear and veneration in Kilcummin churchyard in north Mayo was the *Leac Chuimín*, Cuimín's flagstone. St Cuimín was said to have been washed ashore as an infant in a frail boat and found and adopted by a local man named Maughan. Cuimín adopted a religious hermit's life when he grew up and built his little church which gave the name Kilcumnin to the spot. On his deathbed, he is said to have bequeathed the flagstone to be placed over his grave to the Maughan family, together with the power to use the stone for cursing slanderers and evil doers. If anybody for miles around felt badly wronged by a neighbour, he had first to fast for fifteen days and then employ the Maughan in charge of the *Leac Chuimín* if he wanted to avail of the powers of the *Leac* to get even with the one he felt had wronged him. A walk around St Cuimín's well nearby was also included in the rituals before the curse functionary. A Maugham always turned the stone and intoned the curse for a stiff fee.

In the course of time, the Loughneys, another local sept who had intermarried with the Maughans, claimed a right to use the stone which was becoming a lucrative possession. Feuds and faction fights ensued especially on the annual pattern day in Kilcumnin and this went on for generations. Nearly a hundred and fifty years ago in the 1830s, the son of a local parson named Waldron decided that the stone was bringing the district into disrepute because of all the fights and squabbles of which it was now the centrepiece. He took a sledge hammer at night and broke the stone to fragments. This caused a rush to collect the fragments to use them for the same purposes as the original stone – to curse one's enemies. The situation became so bad that Dean Lyons, then Administrator of Ballina Cathedral had the fragments of the stone collected and built into the masonry of the new cathedral where they have remained since.

THE LAD FROM INISHKEA

North and South Inishkea islands, off the west Mayo coast, were a noted nursery for a hardier than average type of west of Ireland manhood. This hardihood sprang from a harsh and unrelenting struggle for survival with primitive boats and equipment in stormy seas. The rocky inhospitable soil of the islands and the long row to the mainland helped to add to the islanders' unceasing struggles and worries. The inhabitants of the two islands were taken to the mainland and allotted holdings of land by the Irish Land Commission about four decades ago.

Prior to their migration, the people on the neighbouring mainland like to indulge in jokes reflecting the gullibility and innocence of the islanders. One such story was told of a young lad from Inishkea who came to visit relatives in the mainland parish of Ballycroy. In those relatives' house, he saw a round earthenware jar minus the handle. On questioning his host about the jar, the lad from Inishkea was told that the jar was a mare's egg, and that if it were placed on a hob or some warm spot by the fire and turned regularly, a young horse foal would emerge after eleven months.

When leaving for home, the young lad was presented with the jar by his host as a memento of his visit. The jar, bound around with a straw rope, was placed on his back as he left in high spirits for Inishkea. The day being warm and the journey to the ferry for Inishkea a lengthy one, the young visitor soon grew tired and sat down to rest on top of a steep hill. As he sat down, the jar slipped out of the straw rope and rolled rapidly down the hill-side, crashed into a large rock and broke into fragments. Immediately a hare resting on the other side of the rock took flight at top speed, with the lad from Inishkea watching with admiration, as no hares exist on Inishkea. Concluding that the hare was the horse foal released from the mare's egg by the crash, he exclaimed in Irish, *'M'anam 'on diabhal*, when he is a two year old, the devil out of hell won't catch him.'

* * * * *

Another tall tale about a lad from Inishkea and also involving a hare was one of my grandfather's special yarns. As I am not committing myself to say how much of the story is to be believed, I will tell it in his own words.

'In my young days,' said my grandfather, 'I once hired a *spailpín fánach* who called on me in search of work. He was a native of Inishkea. He was a fine, supple, lively lad, every footstep about two yards long when walking. His name was Manus Lavelle. One summer morning we went out early to take some lambs to the fair of Claremorris. On the previous evening, I showed him a steep sandpit with a narrow sloping entrance. I told him that I wanted the sheep and lambs flocked into the sandpit the next morning, in order to pick out the fattest lambs for the fair. The lad was out in good time next morning and after a quick breakfast went off to round up the sheep, while I waited to milk the cows before going to his assistance. When I got to the sandpit, I found he had the sheep already gathered in and among them a large panting hare. "Oh Manus!" I exclaimed, "you have a hare along with the sheep." "Oh," coolly replied Manus, "is that what you call him? Well believe me, that little devil gave me more trouble than all the rest."'

* * * * *

The yarn of the mare's egg, still popular in Ballycroy, must be a very old one as it was related by Maxwell in his *Wild Sports of the West* written nearly a hundred and eighty years ago.

A TALE OF BARNALYRA WOOD

A film director on the look-out for a suitable setting for an eerie film would probably regard Barnalyra, about five miles south-east of Swinford, County Mayo, as an ideal location. The extensive woods that once covered the bleak hills and steep gorges have practically disappeared. Most of the trees remaining are stunted, twisted or commercially useless specimens which seem to resemble brooding spectral sentinels guarding a shady past and adding to the loneliness of the locality. It is small wonder then that Barnalyra can boast of a unique ghost of its own with the unusual name of the *Béicheadán.*

A couple of centuries ago, according to local legend, a poor cottier and his wife lived in a clearing in Barnalyra Wood along the road which at the time was the main road from Sligo to Galway. In later times this road was the route used by the Bianconi mail coaches travelling from Sligo to Galway. The cottier and his wife had a daughter, an only child who grew up to be a remarkably handsome girl and was acclaimed the belle at every local *céilí* and crossroads gathering. The cottier and his wife felt that with such a beautiful daughter and no money for her dowry they were cruelly slighted by Providence. It became an obsession with them that owing to their poverty she would eventually marry some local herd or gamekeeper and spend her life in poverty and drudgery.

One summer evening, a passing stranger called and asked for a meal and if possible a bed for the night, promising to pay well. He said he had been at sea for some years, and having left his ship at Sligo, he hoped to visit his aged parents at the southern end of the County Mayo. The couple gladly agreed to his request. Saying that he felt tired and footsore the sailor retired to the little room pointed out to him by his hostess. On peeping into the room through a chink in the door some time later, the cottier saw his visitor counting a neat pile of golden coins by a slit which served as a window in the bedroom. The cottier and his wife decided that this was a golden opportunity to provide their daughter with a dowry.

They first sent the daughter to stay overnight with an aunt who lived a mile distant. When night fell, they stealthily entered their visitor's bedroom and took his life. Then they buried his body in the nearby wood, and to prevent identification, they buried his head in the nearby Curragh Buí bog. After a few days had lapsed, stories began to circulate about a headless man being seen rushing along the road by Barnalyra wood after nightfall. Many people scoffed at the tale but gradually even the most incredulous of the local people admitted having seen the headless ghost which in time they named the *Béicheadán*, the Screamer.

The fame or fear of the *Béicheadán* grew to such an extent that no local people could be found on the road after nightfall. When local mothers indulged in the hateful old Irish custom of frightening their children with tales of ghosts or pookas, they told them that if they were not indoors and in bed by nightfall the *Béicheadán* would get them. Incidentally young children were ordered to bed early to save food in those hard times. The drivers of the Bianconi mail coaches plying between Sligo and Galway always strove to be clear of Barnalyra Wood before nightfall when the story of the *Béicheadán* gained more publicity. According to the legend, the cottier and his wife met untimely deaths. The cottier was killed by a tree he was felling and his wife's body was found in the stream that flows parallel with the road through the wood after a flood a year later. She told the terrible secret of the sailor's murder to her daughter some time before her death. The daughter lost her reason and pined away and died a short time after her mother.

The legend of the *Béicheadán* lingered on down to comparatively recent times. In 1924 a very wet summer created a fuel scarcity and this, coupled with the unsettled state of the country, resulted in Barnalyra Wood almost disappearing in a few months. People within a ten mile radius of Barnalyra flocked to the wood, ostensibly for firewood, but as most of the timber was first class larch, beech and pine, a very small fraction was used for firewood.

CAPTAIN GALLAGHER

The Irish highwaymen who lived mostly over the later half of the eighteenth century may be regarded as a more commercialised version of the Irish Rapparees. The Rapparees were mainly dispossessed landowners who had to make way for a newer set of Crown favourites and adventurers. This forced the dispossessed landowners to take to the woods and hills with as many followers as they could muster and wreak vengeance on the new set of landlords and other landowners. The Rapparees in their campaign against the new set of Planters and the English Crown flourished mainly from the collapse of the 1641 rebellion to the middle of the eighteenth century.

The highwaymen who followed them could be called more proletarian in origin and outlook. Many of them had gained a knowledge of firearms through membership at one time or association with English military or militia units. Some highwaymen carried out raids and holdups of mail coaches singly while others operated with a small band of followers rarely exceeding half a dozen. To the latter category belonged Captain Gallagher, the famous County Mayo highwayman. He was a native of Bonniconlon but spent part of his youthful days with an aunt in the townland of Derryronane, Swinford, near the wood of Barnalyra.

When he decided on a freebooting career he picked three or four companions. Equipped with fast horses and the erratic blunderbusses of the period, they ranged over all east Mayo and parts of south Sligo and west Roscommon. In addition to the holding up and robbing of the mail coaches, they raided the houses of landlords and other wealthy people. On one occasion, they raided the home of a particularly hated landlord in Killasser, and in addition to seizing all his silver and other valuables, they compelled him to chew up and swallow eviction notices he had prepared for half a dozen of his tenants. After some narrow escapes from the English soldiers, Captain Gallagher's luck finally ran out. He was spending a quiet Christmas recovering from illness in a friend's house in the parish of Coolcarney or Attymass among the foot-hills of the Ox Mountains. A jealous neighbour of his host, a man whom Captain Gallagher had former-ly helped, sent a message to the commanding officer of the Redcoats in Foxford that Captain Gallagher was staying in a house beside his in Attymass.

The officer sent messages to the military station-ed in Ballina, Castlebar and Swinford for assistance before attempting the capture. With a force of nearly two hundred men, the Redcoats surrounded the house. Being ill and in order to save his host and his family, the highwayman surrendered with-out resistance. He was rushed to Foxford and after a hasty sham trial was sentenced to be hanged and taken to Castlebar to have the sentence carried out.

Questioned before mounting the scaffold, the Captain asserted that all his treasure was hidden under a rock in Barnalyra. Hearing this, the officer in charge hastily carried out the execution and then dashed towards the wood of Barnalyra with a hand-picked squad of cavalry. Doubless, visions of new-found wealth or rewards from the Crown helped to hurry them on. When they reached Barnalyra they found to their dismay not the few rocks they had visioned but countless thousands of rocks of all shapes and sizes. After some days' search, all they found was a jewel-hilted sword. Possibly the puzzle about the location of Captain Gallagher's treasure may never be solved. Some people believe that his confession was made in the hope that he would be taken to Barnalyra to point out the rock in question. He knew that his companions were staying in a hideout on the Derryronane-Curryane border close to the wood and he may have had hopes of a rescue attempt by them.

DUDLEY COSTELLO

Barnalyra Wood had the distinction of being a favourite hideout for the noted Rapparee Dudley Costello one century before it served as the headquarters of Captain Gallagher and his small outlawed band.

The Costellos were one of the earliest Norman

families to settle in Mayo and in time had intermarried with the MacDermotts, O'Garas and other leading native Irish families and had adopted native customs and manners. For this they incurred the enmity of the English authorities in Ireland, and after the collapse of the 1641 rebellion, their lands were gradually seized by the Crown forces and parcelled out to the latest set of Crown favourites. Most of the Costello lands were given to the Dillons. Other east Mayo families to suffer a similar fate were the Anglo-Norman Jordans and Burkes who lost a good deal of their lands to the Brownes, Ormsby, Cuffes, Jones's, etc. Around 1660 the chief of the Costellos, Dualta Costello (anglicised Dudley Costello), seeing his estates whittled down to a few acres around Castlemore near the modern town of Ballaghaderreen, decided on open revolt against the English Crown. Gathering a few dozen followers, many of them veterans who had fought on the Continent and in the 1641 rebellion, he took to the woods and the hills harrying the new planters with fire and sword. His operations extended over all the country between Lough Erne in Fermanagh and Lough Mask in Mayo. The State Papers of the period refer to him as 'The Scourge of Mayo'.

In addition to burning the mansions of his enemies, he drove off their cattle to inaccessible woods, mountains and swamps. In 1667 he carried out a big cattle raid on the planter's estate in *Cruachán Gailing* in the parish of Killasser. While driving the cattle in the general direction of Barnalyra Wood, Dudley Costello and his men were ambushed at one of the River Moy fords at Tumgesh. Costello was killed by a lucky shot from Captain Dillon's gun but the rest of his party, including his second in command Captain Nangle escaped. Dudley Costello's head was sent to Dublin and placed on a spike for a year and a day outside St James's prison, now Guinness's brewery. Over the head was the inscription 'The Scourge of Mayo'. There is another version of Dudley Costello's death which gives his native Castlemore as the scene of the fatal encounter in which he met his death. However, a letter written by Captain Dillon (whose brother got most of the Costello lands) to the Governor of Connacht mentions a crossing on the 'Moy Water' as the location of the ambush by the Crown forces.